ANTONÍN DVOŘÁK

VIOLIN CONCERTO

A minor/a-Moll/la mineur
Op. 53

Ernst Eulenburg Ltd
London · Mainz · Madrid · New York · Paris · Prague · Tokyo · Toronto · Zürich

CONTENTS

Ernst Eulenburg Ltd
48 Great Marlborough Street
London W1F 7BB

PREFACE

Smetana (1824–1884) and Dvořák (1841–1904) are the founders of national Czech music as a school in the 19th century. Both had a profound liking for the opera as the most characteristic form of the romantic national style. Smetana created national Czech operas and even his 'Bartered Bride' has become the peasant opera par excellence for the whole musical world. On the other hand none of Dvořák's eleven operas had a lasting success. But all the same in his works one can find many proofs of talent for the lyric-poetical, the oratoric-choral and the dramatic-programmatic.

The special character of Dvořák's instrumental style is marked by the deeply rooted relation to the music of his people together with the studied form of classical music. The Czech village and the constructive spirit of the Beethoven Sonata are the latent poles of Dvořák's inspiration. The natural musician of the people is here closely connected with the artist of form of nearly classical severity. Therefore it was possible for Dvořák to create a significant and imposing basis to the Czech music under the influence of the conscious national revival not only with works for chamber music, but also with concertos for instruments as well as symphonies, overtures, etc.

The Concerto for Violin in A minor, Op.53, was composed in the period from July till the middle of September 1879. Dvořák dedicated it to the great Hungarian-German violinist, Joseph Joachim, who, in the same year, had played two works of Dvořák at the Chamber Music Concerts in Berlin.

At the request of the composer Joachim looked the score through. It has not been forgotten how many alterations had been requested and obtained by Joachim from his friend Brahms in the latter's Concerto for Violin. Therefore it is not astonishing that, according to a letter of Dvořák to his publisher Simrock in 1882, his Concerto for Violin remained full two years in the hands of Joachim until the scores for solo and orchestra accompaniment were altered and finally set down by the composer, who, by the way, was quite willing to comply with Joachim's wishes. How far these alterations differed technically from the original or as regards so style is now impossible to ascertain. Curiously enough, Joachim never played this concerto in public, although dedicated to him. In 1883 it was published by Simrock and in october of the same year it was executed for the first time by the Czech violinist František Ondříček in Prague.

The composition is so full of temperament, so lyrical and melodious and with such rhythmic verve that until 1900 it was one of the most played concertos of its type. The symphonic character does not suffer through the rather short construction of the first Allegro movement, not through the more broad construction of the Adagio movement, both linked together by a theme, so that the lyrical side is predominant. The energetic Allegro actually only develops the principal theme divided up between the orchestra and the soloist (b5).

In the plain melancholy Adagio in F major there are contrasts in the minor key (bb41, 57 and 108) and beautifully modulating transitions (to D major b69, to E major b79, to A flat major b112).

In the final Rondo in A major which is full of beautiful dance rhythm, real Slavic

IV

'Furiant Allegro' and 'Dumky[1]-Andante' elements are characteristically contrasted (bb363 and 743). The four Intermezzo ideas are in F sharp major (b127), D minor (b363) and A major (bb544 and 743).

Antoine-E. Cherbuliez

---

[1] Plural of Dumka [diminutive of Ukrainian duma 'thought', 'folk song'], Duma: lyrical folk song of elegiac character, also – as classical form – pensive, introverted composition.

VORWORT

Smetana (1824–1884) und Dvořák (1841–1904) sind die Begründer der national-tschechischen Tonschule des 19. Jahrhunderts. Beide teilten die Liebe zur Oper, der charakteristischsten Form der romantischen Nationalstile. Smetana schuf mit seinen Bühnenwerken tschechische Nationalopern und mit der *Verkauften Braut* auch außerhalb seiner engeren Heimat das Ideal einer bäuerlichen Volksoper. Hingegen war keiner der elf Opern Dvořáks ein dauernder Erfolg beschieden. Dennoch finden sich in Dvořáks Werken zahlreiche lyrisch-poetische, oratorisch-chorische und dramatisch-programmatische Talentproben.

Der besondere Charakter von Dvořáks Instrumentalstil ist durch die Verbindung eines tief verwurzelten Verhältnisses zum einheimischen Volksmusikgut mit dem bewussten Studium der Form der klassischen Musik gekennzeichnet. Das tschechische Dorf und der konstruktive Geist der Beethoven'schen Sonate sind die latenten Pole von Dvořáks Inspiration und Gestaltung. Der naturhafte Vollblutmusikant verbindet sich bei ihm eng mit dem Formkünstler von fast klassischer Strenge. Dies ermöglichte Dvořák, der tschechischen Musik im Zeichen ihrer bewussten nationalen Erneuerung nicht nur mit Kammermusikwerken, sondern auch mit seinen Instrumentalkonzerten, neben Sinfonien, Ouvertüren usw. eine bedeutsame großformatige Grundlage zu schaffen. Für Violine, Klavier und Violoncello schrieb Dvořák acht orchesterbegleitete Werke, darunter ein Klavierkonzert, ein Violinkonzert und zwei Cellokonzerte.

Das Violinkonzert in a-Moll op. 53, entstand in der Zeit von Juli bis Mitte September 1879. Dvořák widmete es dem großen ungarisch-deutschen Geiger Josef Joachim, der in seinen Berliner Kammermusikkonzerten im gleichen Jahre zwei Werke Dvořáks aufgeführt hatte.

Joachim sah auf Wunsch des Komponisten die Partitur durch. Man erinnert sich, wie viele Änderungen Joachim am Violinkonzert seines Freundes Brahms wünschte und durchsetzte. Es ist daher verständlich, dass Dvořáks Konzert nach eigener Aussage in einem Brief an seinen Berliner Verleger Simrock von 1882 volle zwei Jahre bei Joachim blieb, bis Solostimme und Orchesterbegleitung von dem bereitwillig darauf eingehenden Komponisten bereinigt waren. In welchem Maße die ursprüngliche Fassung technisch oder gar stilistisch verändert wurde, lässt sich jetzt nicht mehr feststellen. Eigentümlicherweise hat Joachim das ihm gewidmete Konzert nie öffentlich gespielt. 1883 erschien es bei Simrock und im Oktober dieses Jahres hob es der tschechische Geiger František Ondříček in Prag aus der Taufe.

Die temperamentvolle, lyrisch blühende und rhythmisch mitreißende, dazu klanglich intensive Tonsprache machen das Stück zu einem der vor und um 1900 meistgespielten Werke seiner Gattung. Sein sinfonischer Charakter leidet nicht durch die ziemlich knappe Anlage des ersten Allegro-Satzes oder die eher breite des unmittelbar damit durch eine Überleitung verbundenen Adagio-Satzes, sodass das Lyrische deutlich überwiegt.

Das energische Allegro entwickelt im Grunde nur das zwischen Orchester und Solist (T. 5) aufgeteilte Hauptthema. Im schlicht-schwermütigen Adagio (in F-Dur) sind Mollkontraste (T. 41, 57, 108) und schöne modulatorische Ausweichungen (nach D-Dur T. 69, nach E-Dur T. 79, nach As-Dur T. 112) eingebaut.

Im glänzenden, tänzerisch rhythmisierten Finalrondo (in A-Dur) sind echt slawische „Furiant-Allegro- und Dumky[1]-Andante-Elemente" (T. 363, 743) wirksam gegenübergestellt. Die vier Intermezzogedanken stehen in Fis-Dur (T. 127), d-Moll (T. 363) und A-Dur (T. 544 und 743).

Antoine-E. Cherbuliez

---

[1] Plural von Dumka [Diminutivum zu ukrainisch duma „Gedanke", „Volkslied"], Duma: lyrisches Volkslied elegischen Charakters, auch – als klassische Form – in sich versunkene Komposition.

VIOLIN CONCERTO

I

Antonín Dvořák
(1841–1904)
Op. 53

Allegro ma non troppo

No. 751   EE 4665

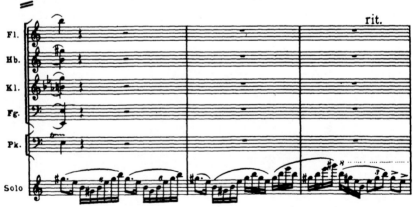

E. E. 4665

6

8

80

24

26

E. E. 4665

E. E. 4665

II

Adagio ma non troppo

Un poco tranquillo, quasi Tempo I

48

E. E. 4665

58

III. Finale

66

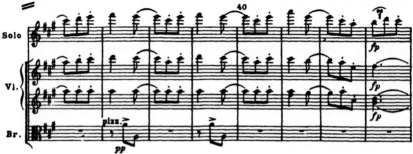

E. E. 4665

E. E. 4665

E. E. 4665

78

E. E. 4665

79

E. E. 4665

E. E. 4665

E. E. 4665

94

E. E. 4665

poco a poco cresc.

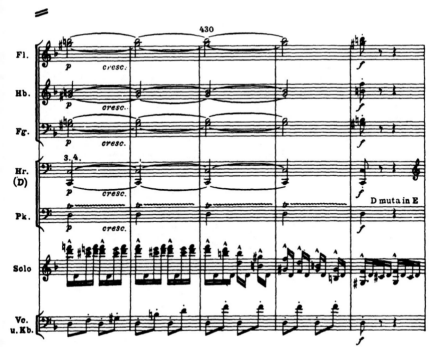

E. E. 4665

E. E. 4665

E. E. 4665

L'istesso tempo (♩=♩.)

Tempo I

poco accelerando